KU-428-326

PARIS
NIGHT & DAY
COLOURING BOOK

THIS IS A SEVENOAKS BOOK

Published by SevenOaks
An imprint of Carlton Books Ltd
20 Mortimer Street
London W1T 3JW

Copyright © 2016 Carlton Books Ltd

All rights reserved. No part of this publication may be reproduced, stored in a
retrieval system, or transmitted in any form or by any means, electronic, mechanical,
photocopying, recording or otherwise, without the prior permission of the copyright
owner and the publishers.

A CIP catalogue record for this book is available from the British Library

10 9 8 7 6 5 4 3 2 1

ISBN 978-1-78177-548-6

Printed in China

PARIS

NIGHT & DAY

COLOURING BOOK

ILLUSTRATED BY PATRICIA MOFFETT

SEVENOAKS

CONTENTS

ARC DE TRIOMPHE

PALAIS GARNIER

CHÂTEAU DE VERSAILLES

TOUR EIFFEL

SACRÉ-COEUR

NOTRE-DAME

PLACE DE LA CONCORDE

PARC DES BUTTES-CHAUMONT

MÉTROPOLITAIN

MUSÉE BOURDELLE

MUSÉE DU LOUVRE

VERSAILLES COUR DE MARBRE

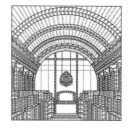

MUSÉE D'ORSAY

PLACE DE LA BASTILLE

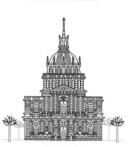

HÔTEL DES INVALIDES

MOULIN ROUGE

PANTHÉON

CENTRE POMPIDOU

JARDIN DES TUILERIES

PONT NEUF

**JARDIN
DES PLANTES**

PALAIS-ROYAL

**PONT
ALEXANDRE III**

SAINTE-CHAPELLE

CONCIERGERIE

PLACE VENDÔME

PARC MONCEAU

GRAND PALAIS

**DÔME DES
INVALIDES**

**CIMETIÈRE DU
PÈRE-LACHAISE**

**TOUR
MONTPARNASSE**

MUSÉE RODIN

**PARC DU CHAMP
DE MARS**

ÎLE DE LA CITÉ

PETIT PALAIS

**GALERIES
LAFAYETTE**

MUSÉE DE CLUNY

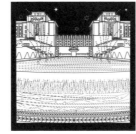

**PALAIS DE
CHAILLOT**

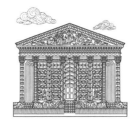

**ÉGLISE DE LA
MADELEINE**

PLACE DES VOSGES

**PARC DE LA
VILLETTE**

PARIS-PLAGES

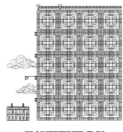

**INSTITUT DU
MONDE ARABE**

QUARTIER LATIN

**JARDIN DES SERRES
D'AUTEUIL**

Introduction

Welcome to a new colouring challenge!

The *Paris Night & Day Colouring Book* is unique because it invites you to colour not just against white, but also blue, black and gold backgrounds. Each of the 90 detailed outlines featured here are displayed against both a day and a night backdrop, providing you with superb opportunities to highlight tone and texture, and create striking contrasts.

While daylight can illuminate subtle motifs and tints, darkness can bring out flashes of colour or the sparkle of lights. In fact, you'll find there's a surprising difference between an enchanting Parisian scene depicted in golden sunshine and that same scene shown against a background of inky darkness.

The captivating sights presented in this book range from impressive buildings to beautiful statues, and from pretty parks to magnificent bridges. They include many favourites, such as the Musée du Louvre, Tour Eiffel, Sacré-Coeur and Notre-Dame, as well as less familiar sights, like the Petit Palais, Institut du Monde Arabe, Tour Montparnasse, Cimetière du Père-Lachaise and Conciergerie. There is the legendary entertainment venue, the Moulin Rouge, and wonderful outdoor spaces, such as the Parc des Buttes-Chaumont, Jardin des Tuileries and Parc Monceau.

What was beautiful in the daytime can seem just as stunning at night, and what was subtle in the light can emerge from darkness as striking when night falls. How will your daylight Quartier Latin differ from your midnight version? Could your daytime Château de Versailles sparkle in the moonlight? Might the Musée Rodin come alive after dark?

How you decide to bring out the appearance of a Parisian scene is determined by you and the colour choices you make on each artwork. You can be as accurate and realistic, or as creative and fantasy-filled, as you like. Working with the coloured backgrounds opens up exciting possibilities and an invigorating new world of colouring, so let your imagination – and your pens – run wild.

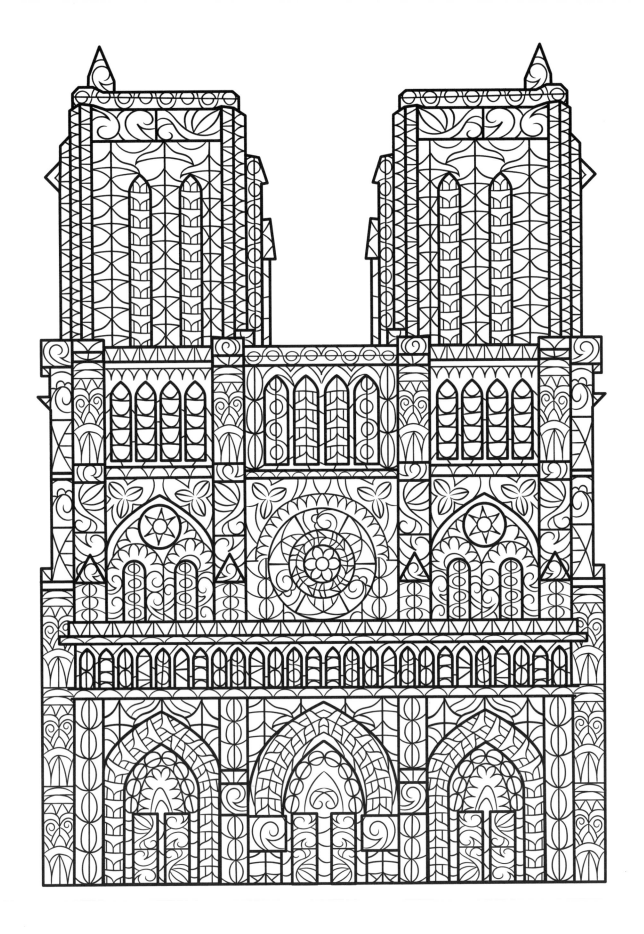

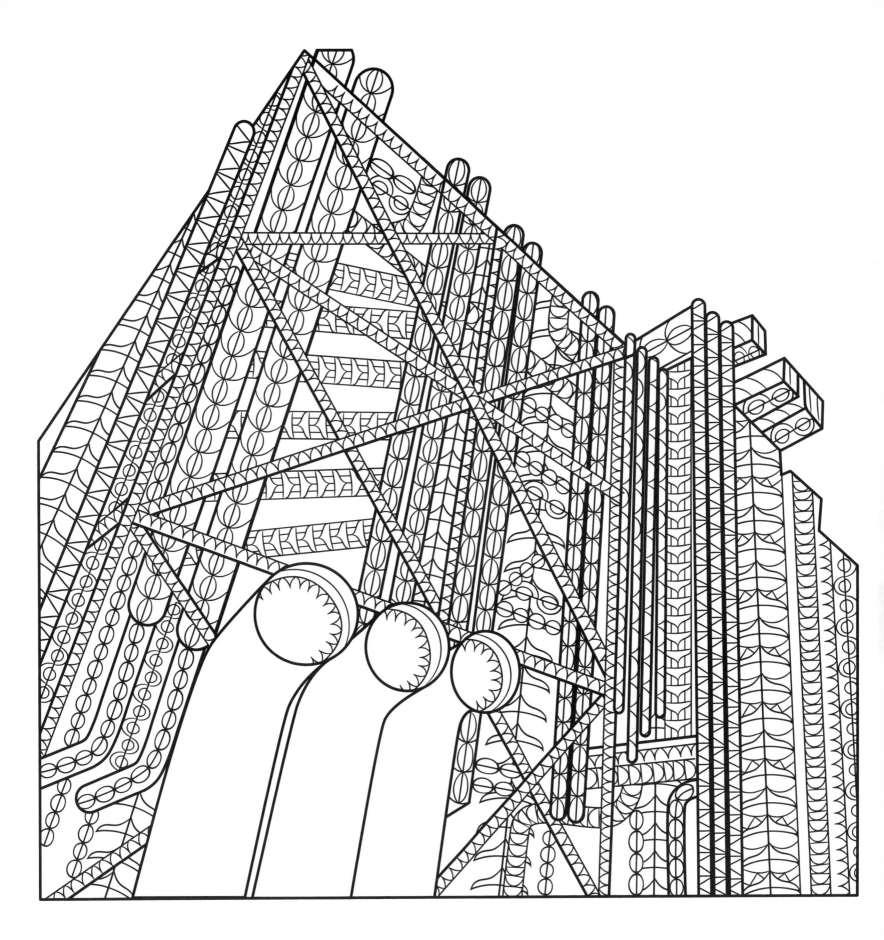

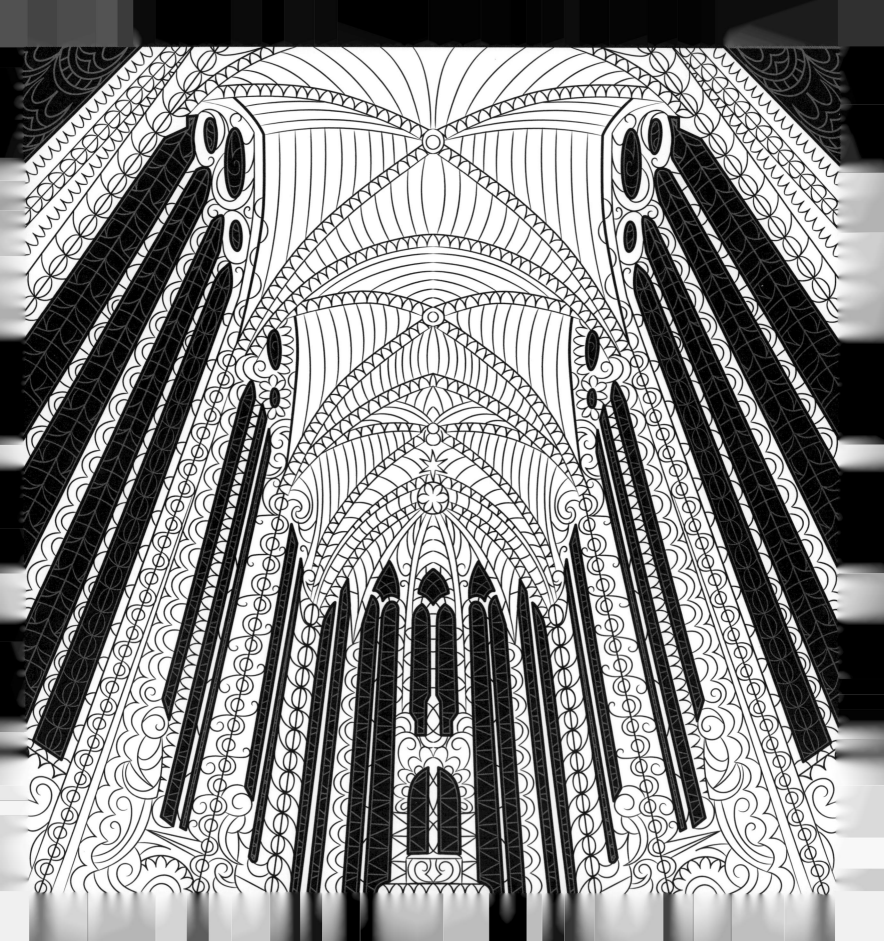

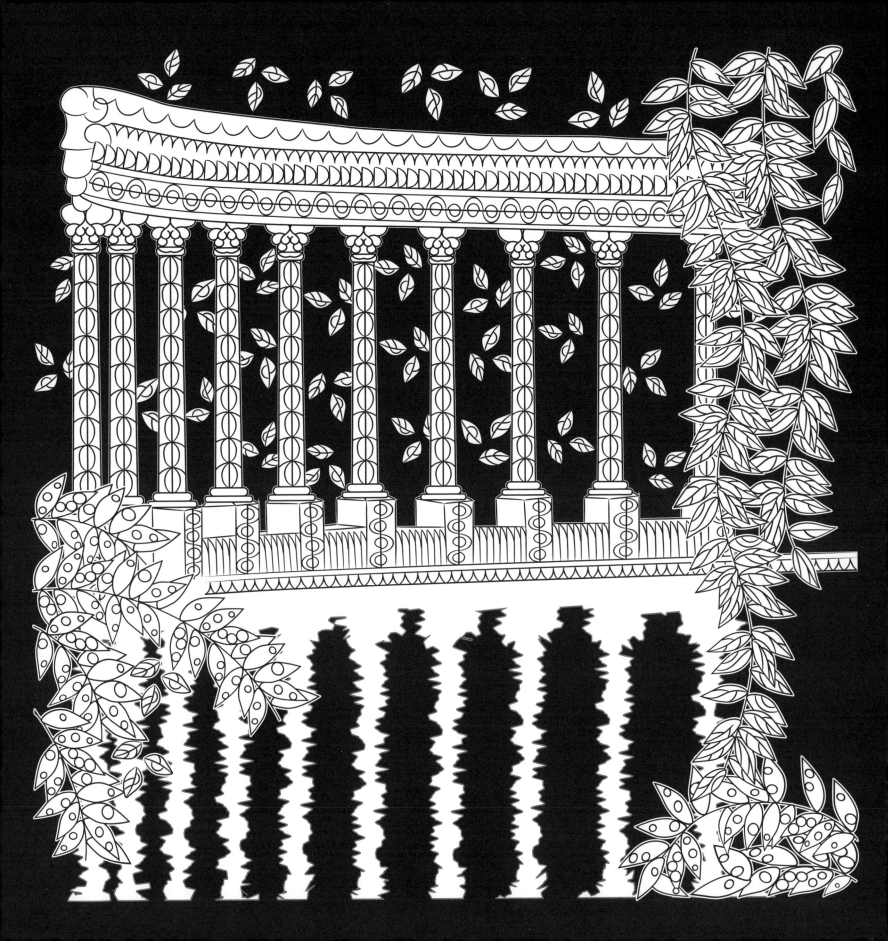

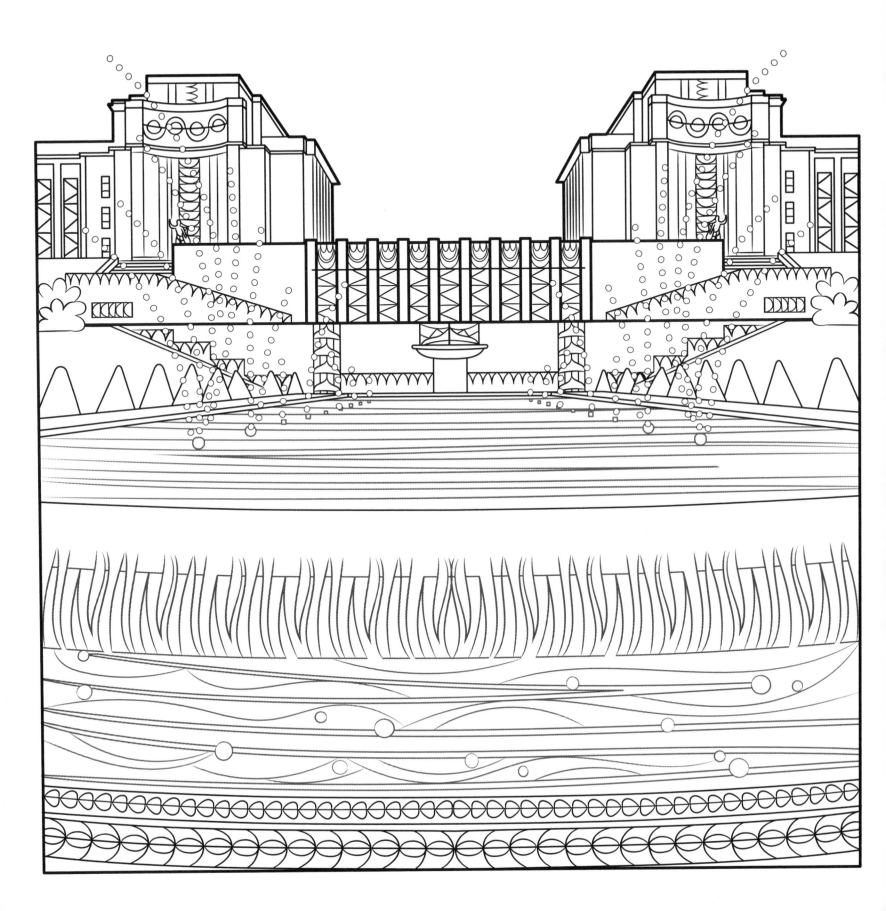

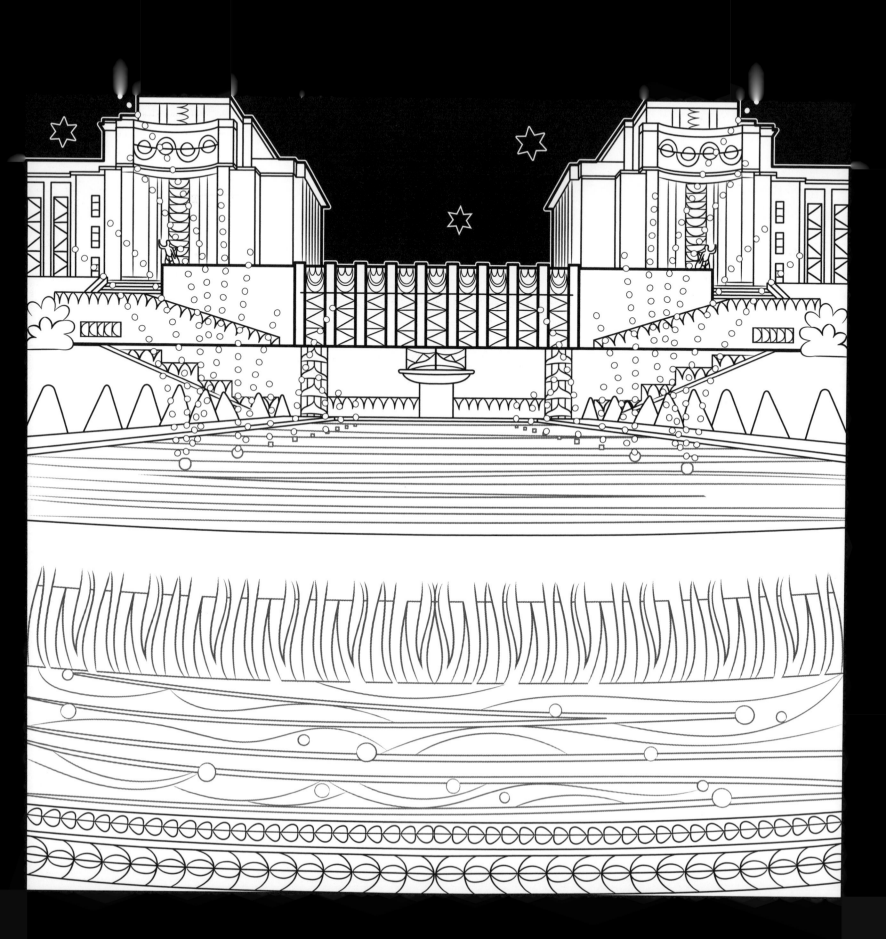

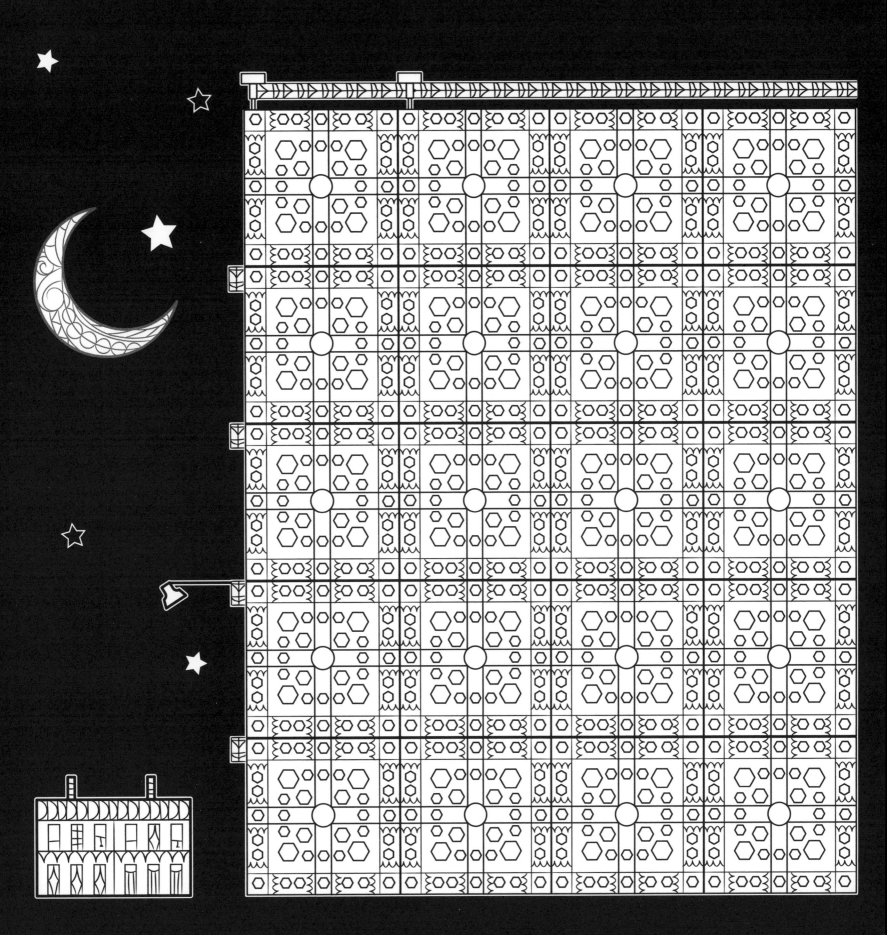

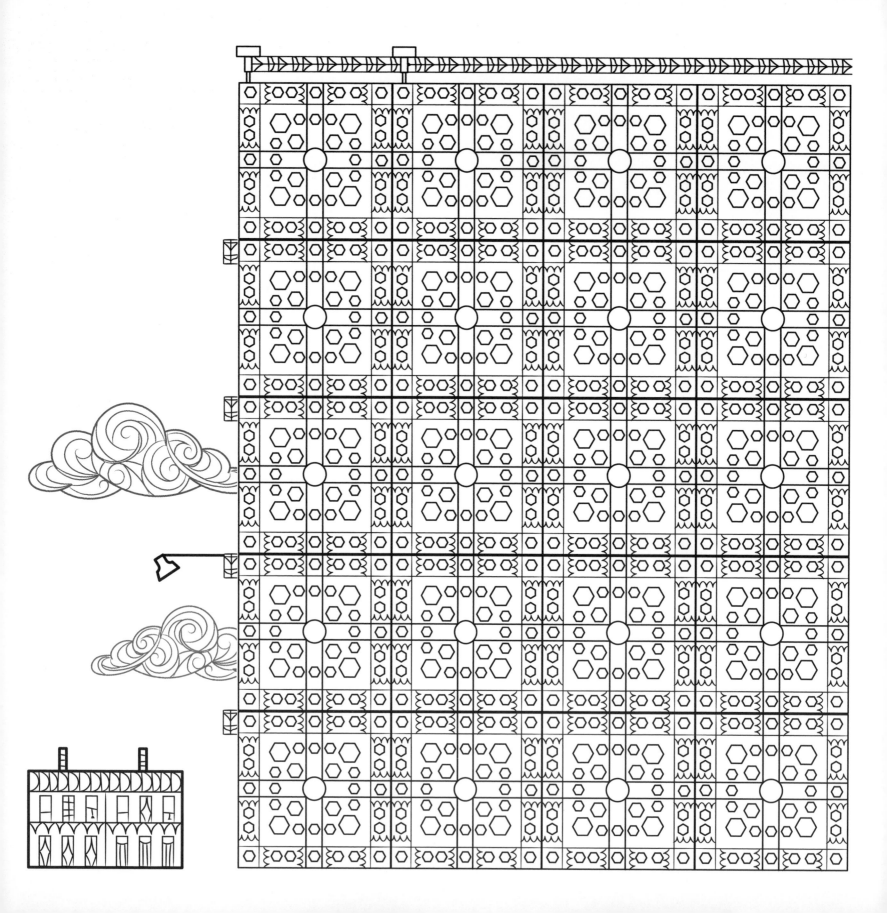